Foxy Red Tail

Book 1
Foxy Learns About the Trees
&
The Cycle of Life

ISBN 9798740740731599

*I dedicate this book to my dear friend **Victoria Illman**.*

Her Friendship, Support, Kindness and Encouragement has enabled me to create & illustrate this book, the first in a series of Foxy Red Tail Books.

Also to all the Granny & Grandads, Parents, Carers and Teachers who love reading to little ones and exploring Nature

*With a special mention to **my own Grandchildren** and other Children and Grandchildren who have touched my heart*

***Christian & Charlotte**, Emma Mark & Luke, Jess & Kieran, Martha & Freda, Poppy & Rubie, Hei Yuen, Max, Alex & Elliot, Camille & Andrea, Robin & Sasha, Louie, Reuben, Tilly, Elouise & Olivia, Joseph & Isabelle, Elodie, Jack & Thomas, Clement, Jamie, Ashley, Freddie, Hazel, Joshua, George Charlotte & Louis, Amber, Kirsty, Ernest, Etta & Rosa, Viaan and all the other wonderful children who have touched my heart*

And for those yet to come...

May your lives be Blessed with Happiness and a Love of our Natural World

POEM - Foxy Red Tail's Journey

Little Foxy Red Tail, Danced the night away,

Chasing after fireflies, running through the hay.

When he heard the gentle call, floating on the breeze;

'Foxy Darling, time for Bed' 'Coming Mother Coming' and with that gave a sneeze!

Little Foxy Red Tail, wakes up with a start,

'Todays the day' he yells, as his brothers gave a bark.

Mother walked him all the way, through different seas of frosted hay,

to Grannies special woodland home where his destination lay!

Little Foxy Red Tail, was moving home you see.

Heading to the woodland where his Granny was to be.

So far away from mother and brothers, but snuggled with his Granny,

Little Foxy Red Tail was about to have adventures, oh so many!

Foxy Red Tail slowly opened his eyes and gave a big yawn.

Stretching his legs, he barked good morning to his Granny.

He wanted to be an explorer today so he decided to go for a long walk, up the steep hill where the tall Conifer Trees stood silhouetted against the sky.

It was Springtime.

Foxy Red tail was so excited to see all the new life sprouting everywhere within the woodland.

He loved exploring in the woods.

This was now his home. He had moved here to live with his Granny, Sylvie Feather Tail, in her cosy home called Red Den.

Red Den was lovely and warm, filled with happy memories of when Foxy would visit as a tiny cub with his family.

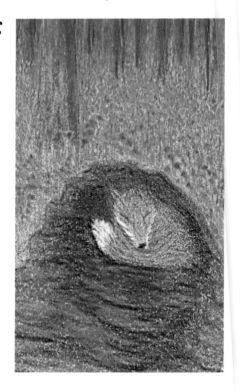

Now he had his very own bed in Granny's Red Den.

It was lined with sweet smelling herbs, bracken and feathers.

Granny Sylvie had collected them all, to make a very deep, squashy, bed for him, with a few sprigs of wild lavender placed here and there, to help him sleep.

Granny Sylvie had promised to teach

Foxy all about the secrets of the woodland.

It was important for him to know, now that he had decided to move home, and live with her in Red Den.

Red Den was right in the middle of Bluebell Wood.

Granny had started to teach Foxy all about his new home by explaining about the different types of trees and their life cycles.

It was so interesting!

Granny loved the woodland and would enjoy teaching Foxy all about the Trees, the plants and animals, the birds, insects, bees and butterflies that all lived happily together in this magical place called Bluebell Wood.

As Foxy popped his head out of the warmth of Red Den into the

morning sunshine he had another stretch before setting off on his adventure.

As he got higher and higher up the steep hill, he noticed a change in the air. It was cooler and quite breezy as the trees began to thin out.

The ground was covered in dried pine cones and needles.

He was also aware of a lovely perfume in the air, produced by the Pine and Spruce trees.

Foxy remembered what Granny Sylvie had taught him about different types of Coniferous trees.

They looked different to the trees that grew around Red Den.

They were darker in colour, and instead of having leaves, they had needles.

He looked up and saw dark green spiky needles!

Some of the trees also had different shaped 'Pine Cones' dotted here and there on their branches.

Some of the pine cones were pointed and some were more rounded, egg shaped. At the base of the straight trunk of the pine trees you could often find last year's pine cones

littering the forest floor.

Granny had explained how the birds and squirrels love to eat the little seeds that are trapped inside the cones. As the pine cones ripen, and start to open, the little seeds are easy to find.

Some of the seeds would be eaten. Some of the seeds would fall on the soft earth.

The wind would blow a carpet of leaves and needles to

cover the seeds, keeping them warm.

The gentle rain would fall and help start the seed to germinate, to change, to swell and grow.

After a while the little seed would split open, and send out a shoot, down into the earth, to search for food and water to help it grow stronger.

Then the little seed would send another shoot upwards towards the sky for warmth from the sun.

Eventually little soft needles would sprout out from the main stem, creating a new baby tree.

Over the years the new baby tree would grow and branches would form.

'Pine Cones' would form, and the whole process will start again.

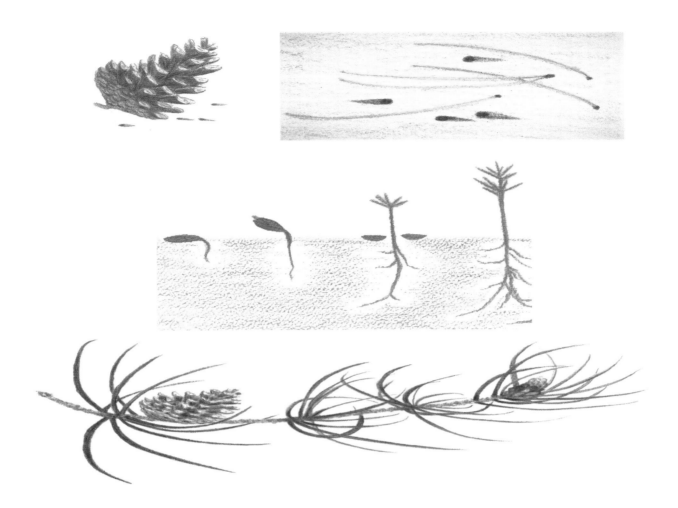

'It's called the 'Cycle of Life'
said Granny.

Granny Sylvie knew so many
interesting things!

Foxy Red Tail was very pleased that Granny had promised to teach him all about the Woodland.

He had already learned so much from her

'What a lucky fox I am.'

He thought to himself.

Foxy decided that he would learn everything he could from his Granny. He loved listening to her.

She was a wonderful teacher!

As he walked further on, he left the trees with needles and cones behind, and started to make his way down the other side of the hill towards a grassy meadow. The meadow was surrounded by a mixture of different trees, with different shaped leaves.

Granny had told Foxy that the type of Trees that grew these leaves were called Deciduous Trees, and that they would change in the Autumn, releasing their leaves, which would dance in the wind and then cover the woodland floor!

Autumn is such a pretty time of year!

Magical!

The leaves would turn to yellows and oranges, golds and browns and even beautiful reds.

Then the special autumn wind
would blow, and the leaves would
fall to the ground, spinning and
swirling around in the wind. Granny

said it was as if they were dancing with the wind.

It was her favourite magical season!

When all the Autumn leaves had fallen to the ground, the trees would go to sleep for the Winter and the leaves would dry out and turn different shades of brown.

After sleeping all Winter long, the woodland trees would wake up again in the Spring.

Tiny green shoots would start to appear, quickly growing to become a canopy of leaves.

Pretty shapes and shades of green, gently waving to each other in the soft, gentle wind all Summer long.

It is another 'Cycle of Life'.

The 'Cycle of the Leaves'.

Foxy remembered everything Granny had said, and was looking forward to seeing the special wind dancing with the leaves, and all the other different seasons of the woodland. But it is

Springtime now, as he continues his walk, noticing the new tiny shoots of green everywhere around him.

Across the meadow, and around the trees, pretty flowers were popping up all over the place. Little yellow  Celandines and tiny Daisies were waving their heads in the breeze surrounded by a sea  of green and a carpet of pretty Bluebells hidding in the grass.

Foxy rested at the edge of the meadow sitting down in the thick blanket of grasses.

He was protected from the breeze here and could feel the warmth of the sun on his back.

Sitting quietly, he suddenly became aware of the birds singing all around him. As foxy looked up to see who was singing the beautiful song, he noticed the Blackbirds and Song Thrushes hopping from branch to branch, singing to each other in such a happy way.

'What a perfect day' he thought to himself. He sat very still so he didn't frighten them away. On the branches of the trees, new leaf buds were bursting open in the warmth of the Spring sunshine.

Spring was beginning
to show itself up
high. Just as Granny
had said it would.

Tiny green pearls of life
were bursting open into baby
leaves.

He thought to himself 'Nature is so
wonderful. It is always changing!'
This was all new to Foxy

because Foxy had come to live with Granny in the Wintertime, when the earth was brown or sometimes white with frost and snow. Trees were bare  and leaves were scattered all over the woodland floor, dry and brown.

Nothing like the beautiful green that cloaked the trees in summer.

Granny had explained that in Springtime some of the trees would have flowers on them,
called Blossom, and the first Blossom to come into bloom was on

the Blackthorn trees then there would be Hawthorn and Cherry Blossom, followed by Apple and Pear Blossom.

The Woodland would be such a colourful place. Filled with blossom and beautiful fragrance.

Granny said that once all the
blossom was
out, the Bees
had a very

important job to
do. She had
explained that
the Bees visit
each blossom,
collecting nectar
for their hives to make into honey,

but those clever little Bees also do another job at the same time.

While they are busy getting deep into the centre of the flowers, to collect the nectar, they brush against the stamens of the flower.

Stamens are covered in pollen.

The pollen looks like yellow dust!

As the busy little Bee pushes his head deep amongst the stamens, to find the nectar, the pollen gets caught in the fur of the Bee's body.

The pollen covers the Bee, then he happily buzzes off to the next flower, and mixes that pollen, with the pollen of the new flower.

The Bees work hard all day collecting the nectar from the flowers and each Bee can visit hundreds of flowers in just one day.

Each visit mixes more pollen!

This mixture of pollen causes the little seed head at the base of the flower to start the process of creating a little 'Fruitlet' to form.

Without the Bees doing such an important job it would be difficult for the pollen to mix. The trees would have to wait for the winds to blow the pollen from blossom to blossom, they wouldn't be able to produce as much fruit as they do with the Bees helping them.

Foxy was fascinated to learn about the blossom and Bees. He hadn't known how important the Bees are, how much they helped the trees.

Granny said that as the blossom dies, the fruit starts to grow and ripen.

This can take many weeks, even months.

Then one day when the fruit is big and ripe, the smallest breeze can

loosen the fruit from the tree, and it falls to the ground.

So, some fruit

gets nibbled away, but some is left on the earth. Then more magic happens and the 'Cycle of Life' starts all over again.

Foxy was beginning to understand more and more about nature and how things grew.

He understood what Granny meant when she talked to him about the amazing

'Cycle of Life'

Foxy loved learning about Trees and how Nature has a 'Cycle of Life' for them all.

 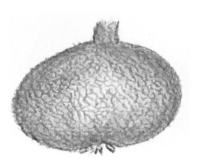 

Foxy sat thinking about the magic of Nature,

and what an enormous part the little Bees have in helping the trees.

Just then a little Bee came and sat on a Daisy right next to him.

Foxy was pleased with everything he had learnt about the trees so far, and the

'Cycles of Life'.

He smiled to himself as he watched the busy Bee flitting from flower to flower noticing the sack of nectar on the back legs of the little Bumble Bee. I am a lucky Fox, he thought, I wonder what secrets of the woodland Granny will tell me about next. Foxy was really looking forward to his next lesson with Granny Sylvie.

Foxy Loves Learning!

As a pair of butterflies danced around the meadow flowers, Foxy noticed

the sky was changing to a pretty pink.

He watched as the sun sank slowly in the sky. 'Goodness, I've been out all day.'

Just at that moment Foxy heard a familiar bark in the distance.

'Time for supper' he

thought as he barked back his response.

He took one last look at the beautiful woodland meadow before trotting all the way back to Granny and 'Red Den' where he would dream about his adventures.

Activities connected to the story.

These activities can be used as a class, or family group, or individually with a carer or teacher.

Create wall art showing the results of the activities, to further deepen understanding, and promote discussion.

Go for a walk in a wooded area, park, school garden, forest, and take a pencil and paper, and perhaps if you can, a camera or phone to take photographs, to refer too later. If this is impossible then use reference books or the internet. Choose a tree to research.

What is your favourite tree and why? Does it have leaves or needles, seeds, fruit or nuts?

Can you draw your favourite tree and all the interesting things you noticed on your walk?

Is it in a woodland, hedgerow, garden or somewhere else? See how many different trees you can see when you go out for a walk, collect different shaped leaves to take home, or back to the classroom, and make a picture with them to add to your wall art..

Draw around them, paint them, stick them, create patterns with them. Are they smooth, can you see veins, what do they feel like?

Use the leaves for Maths, add them up, take them away, sort them into different piles of shape, colour.

Find out the name of the trees you see, find out how big they grow and make a graph from smallest trees to largest?

What else did you notice on your walk? What was the weather like? Were the leaves waving to the wind or dancing free in the wind?

What season is it now where you live? How many seasons are there? What happens to the trees in your area in each season?

Did you notice any birdsong on your walk? What species of bird did you see?

Use your senses, what could you see, hear, smell, what did the trunk of the tree feel like, was any part of the tree edible?

Did you notice any Bees? If so what were they doing? Can you find some twigs and moss to create a Bee hotel?

Did you notice any plants or flowers? If so, do you know the name of the plant or flower? How many different colours of flowers did you notice?

Deeper investigation.

What type of trees grow in your climate and why do they grow there? Research the type of trees in a different climate to yours? Describe how the two climates differ and explain why the vegetation is different? How has the vegetation adapted to its surroundings? What fruit is grown on the trees in your country and in the different climate area you have chosen? Are there any similarities? Name as many fruits, berries and nuts as you can that grow on the 'Trees' in your area?

Now list fruits, berries and nuts that grow on 'Bushes' or 'In the Ground'? Which of these can be eaten by humans? And which can only be eaten by Birds or Animals? (i.e. Berries from a Yew Tree are poisonous to humans but safe for birds) Draw a chart / graph showing your findings? Create a bird feeding area, record what type of birds feed there. Research how to make fat balls, which seeds to use, which seeds do the smaller birds prefer? Research and make a nesting box.

Draw a 'Cycle of Life' diagram of an Apple or a Pine tree, or choose another fruit or tree type.

Take some Bark rubbings of four different trees and label the rubbings. Touch the bark with your eyes closed, what does it feel like? Use descriptive words to discuss/note your findings. Research what type of animal, bird, insect lives in your four trees? Did you notice any signs that an insect had made a home in your trees? Sit or stand in silence what can you hear?

Start a tree diary. Once a month visit your chosen tree and take a photograph or sketch the chosen tree.

Start each chapter with the title of the Month, starting in the month you are in right now. Write down your observations – What do you notice about leaf shape, size, colour? – What birds use the tree to perch or nest in? - Can you see any nests, birds, bees, wasps? – Can you see any crawling insects? - What do you notice around the base of the tree? - What is the ground covered in, plants, leaves, insects, baby trees? – Can you see any roots?

You will start to notice small changes every month, that will build up a picture of the life of the tree. Use your imagination and make your diary colourful and informative. Plant a Tree!

Watch as it changes with the seasons. Spend time outdoors noticing the Nature around you. Bike rides and walking are great ways of enjoying a new connection with Nature.

These are just a few suggestions for you to enjoy as you find out more about the woodland areas around you. See what other activities you can think of as you explore.

Bee Hotel.

You will need a mixture of sticks, small twigs, dried grasses or straw, dried and fresh leaves, moss, twine (scissors to cut the twine into 12 inch/30cm lengths approx. x 2 per person or per bundle), stones or mud.

First start with two pieces of twine laid out on the floor in front of you vertically like this | | about a hand's width apart.

Then collect 6 small twigs about the same length as the twine but place them horizontally across the twine, then add a thin layer of leaves or dried grasses or straw, whatever you can find in your area of woodland or garden.

Then find a thicker stick about 12 inches or 30 centimetres long, with a width of 1 to 2 inches or 2.5 to 5 centimetres and place it on top, in centre of the leaves horizontally.

Then add another layer of 3-4 twigs either side of the stick horizontally.

Then add a thin layer of dried grasses, straw or leaves to cover the twigs.

Then gently pick up each end of one of the pieces of twine and tie the ends together to form a tight bundle, repeat with the other piece of twine.

6 bundles are ideal for your bee hotel, if you have more, you can choose to have more than one site for your bee hotel's. You start to build your Bee Hotel by placing three bundles in the area you want your bee hotel to be, leaving a small gap between them, then place two more bundles on top, in the same direction as the first layer, then a final bundle on the top, 6 bundles in total making a triangle or pyramid shape. Put stones and mud and moss on the side walls of the pyramid, leaving the front and back open for the bees and bugs to crawl into. The stones, mud and moss will stop the wind destroying the shape of the hotel, and protect it from the rain. Once you have made your Bee Hotel you will feel such a sense of achievement knowing that you have done something constructive to help the bees. Experiment with different designs of Bee Hotels. Planting a flower garden is

another way you can help. You can collect seed heads of hedgerow plants that the bees love, and then plant the seeds in a special bee friendly garden. Use your creative skills to make a colourful Bee Friendly sign for your new garden. Research which plants are best to entice the bees to your special Bee garden. Then you can enjoy watching the bees come and feed from the flowers knowing that the pollen will travel with them to all the other flowers they visit that day!

Did you enjoy the Poem at the start of the book about Foxy? Why not write your own Poem about what you saw on your walk? Or the Bees in your garden? Draw a picture to go with it. Make Wall art using your drawings and poems and leaves.

Enjoy Nature!

Note from the Author

I do hope you have enjoyed Foxy Red Tails adventure, as he learns all about the trees and their 'Cycles of Life' and he starts to explore his new Woodland home. Bluebell Wood is full of interesting things that Granny and Foxy will continue to explore in other books in the future. So watch out for new stories coming soon.

Does your school have a Bee friendly garden? Have you have planted a tree? Are you studying a tree? Have you made a Bee Hotel?

There are many interesting organisations that have resources online for you to use, to learn more about Woodland, Woodland creatures, or Woodlands to visit. Here are a few to get you started –

The Woodland Trust	www.woodlandtrust.org.uk
Forestry Commission	www.forestryengland.uk
RSPB	www.rspb.org.uk
National Trust	www.nationaltrust.org.uk
Bee Conservation Trust	www.bumblebeeconservation.org
Buglife	www.buglife.org.uk
Trees for Life	www.treesforlife.org.uk
Learning Through Landscapes	www.ltl.org.uk
Pollinator Partnership	www.pollinator.org

There are many more organisations that you can find as you start to explore Nature and all its glory. I hope you enjoy your journey! Jodi x

Printed in Great Britain
by Amazon